AN OFFICIAL LETTER · AN OFFICIAL LETTER

from the desk of
David Walliams

Dear reader,

Welcome to my world. This book
is all about my stories and
characters. It's a book of stuff.
Fun stuff. Silly stuff. Stuff
that was too naughty to put in my
books. It is NOT for grown-ups.
This book is best read under the
duvet with a torch. Enjoy!

David Walliams

THE LIBRARY OF MR WALLIAMS

TITLE: BOOK OF STUFF

AUTHOR: MR WALLYBUMS

DATE DUE	ISSUED TO
APR 20 10 BC	Cleopatra
NOV 12 1940	Winston Churchill
NOV 1 1599	Guildenstern
DEC 09 1599	Rosencrantz
JUN 20 2008	RAJ

£1,000 FINE IF OVERDUE

First published in Great Britain by
HarperCollins *Children's Books* in 2018
HarperCollins *Children's Books* is a division of HarperCollins*Publishers* Ltd,
HarperCollins Publishers
1 London Bridge Street
London SE1 9GF

The HarperCollins website address is:
www.harpercollins.co.uk

6

Text © HarperCollins Publishers Ltd 2018
Illustrations © Tony Ross 2010, 2011, 2012, 2013, 2014, 2015, 2016, 2017, 2018
Illustrations pp. 14, 15, 44, 45, 50, 51, 58 and 59 © Quentin Blake 2008, 2009, 2018
Cover lettering of author's name and back cover illustrations
© Quentin Blake 2008, 2009, 2010
All rights reserved.

ISBN 978–0–00–829325–3

Tony Ross and Quentin Blake assert the moral right to be identified
as the illustrators of the work.

Printed and bound in the UK by Bell & Bain Ltd, Glasgow

WITH SPECIAL THANKS TO THE DAWSON BROS.

THE WORLD OF David Walliams

BOOK OF STUFF

With illustrations from
Quentin Blake
and
Tony Ross

HarperCollins *Children's Books*

WELCOME TO
the world of
David Walliams

This book of stuff is full of everything you never wanted to know about David Walliams. For those of you not familiar with books, here is a quick guide on how to use one:

 1 Buy this book from a shop.

 2 Don't try to switch on this book. There is NO ON switch. It's a BOOK.

 3 Do not try to tap or swipe the book. It's a BOOK.

 4 Do not try to adjust the volume or brightness of this book. It's a BOOK.

 5 DO open this book. It's a BOOK.

 6 Read the words that are written on the page.

 7 If you run out of words on the page, turn the page.

 8 If you run out of words on the page and there isn't another page, you must have finished reading the book. WELL DONE!

 9 If you don't know how to read, then you're probably NOT reading this. Get someone to read it to you!

TIP
To turn up the brightness, read it outside.

TIP
If a word appears to be upside down, check to see if you are upside down.

I, the reader, named _____ , agree that this book should forever remain the rightful property of

David Walliams

but will be kept in my room, and he should be allowed to have it back at any time should he want to read it.

This book was bought by _____

and my favourite flavour of crisps is _____.

Signed _____

LOADS OF CONTENTS

William Shakespeare Esq.

Good morrow to thou, most beloved reader, and welcome to the world of David Walliams Book of Stuffeth

Whence I was asked to writeth the introduction to this book by the illustrious scribe David Walliams, I squealethed with delightment. "David Walliams knows who I, humble Williameth of Shakespeare, do be!" Or, as I once famously wroteth in one of my too-longeth plays: "Do be, or not do be?"

When a teachereth would make me read a booketh at school, I would oftenly say, "Nay, good teacher! I shall not read any of your plopeth-filled pages. For I, Sir William Shakespeare, declare that words are for nerds. And I am not a nerd. I am a cool dude." Yet, one dew-filled morn, whileth I wended my way through my local bookshop, located betwixt the chippy and the newsies, I chanced upon the *Mr Stinketh* novel. It was from henceforth I thought: This truly is the finest writer in the English, or indeed any, language. I prostrate myself before his magnificence and do dreameth of one day perchance writing something with just one morsel of this greatness.

Oh, what inspiration! I immediately quitteth my paper round and pickethed up my quill (which is basically like a feather biro) and began to writeth myself.

There would be no *Romeo and Juliet* without *Gangsta Granny*. There would be no *Hamlet* without *Ratburger*. And I am happyeth to confess that the character of King Lear is just blatantly rippedeth offeth from the greatest literary creation of all time, Raj the newsagent.

I owe my whole career to David Walliams, as indeed do Charleseth of Dickens, Janeth Austenment, Lewith Carroll, Roaleth Dahleth and Enid Blytington.

In facteth, David is sucheth an inspirationmentment that I have changed my name, henceforth, herewith and from now on, to Walliam Shakespeare. Good morrow to you.

Yours sincerelyeth,

Walliam
Shakespeare

P.S. I know I died four hundred years ago, but this is really me, honest.

ANSWERS ON PAGE 76

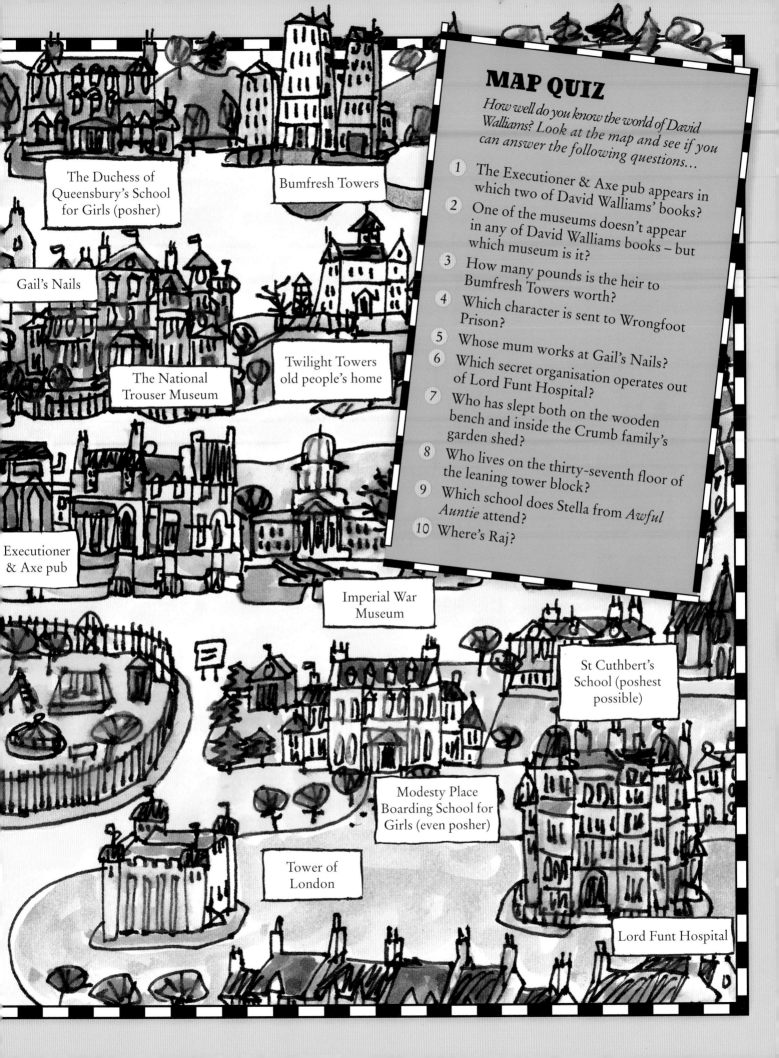

The Duchess of Queensbury's School for Girls (posher)

Bumfresh Towers

Gail's Nails

The National Trouser Museum

Twilight Towers old people's home

Executioner & Axe pub

Imperial War Museum

St Cuthbert's School (poshest possible)

Modesty Place Boarding School for Girls (even posher)

Tower of London

Lord Funt Hospital

MAP QUIZ

How well do you know the world of David Walliams? Look at the map and see if you can answer the following questions…

1 The Executioner & Axe pub appears in which two of David Walliams' books?

2 One of the museums doesn't appear in any of David Walliams books – but which museum is it?

3 How many pounds is the heir to Bumfresh Towers worth?

4 Which character is sent to Wrongfoot Prison?

5 Whose mum works at Gail's Nails?

6 Which secret organisation operates out of Lord Funt Hospital?

7 Who has slept both on the wooden bench and inside the Crumb family's garden shed?

8 Who lives on the thirty-seventh floor of the leaning tower block?

9 Which school does Stella from *Awful Auntie* attend?

10 Where's Raj?

WHICH David Walliams

Once you've found out who you are, ask your friends and family who they are too!

Are you a child?
— YES →
— NO ↓

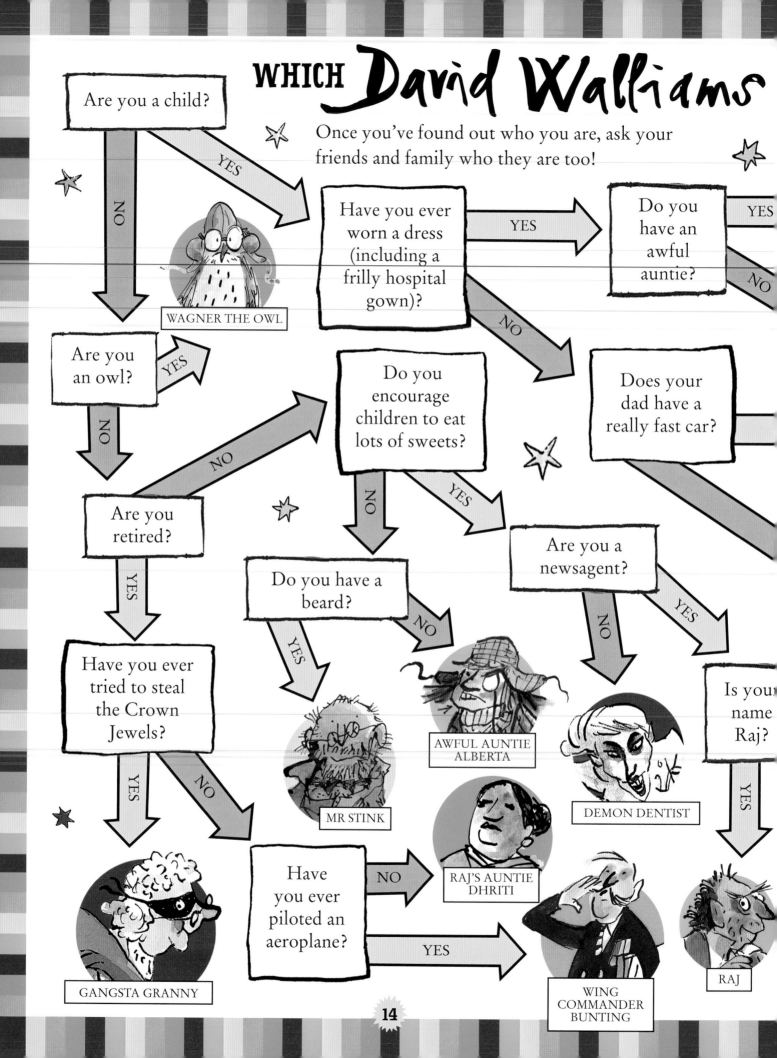
WAGNER THE OWL

Have you ever worn a dress (including a frilly hospital gown)?
— YES →
— NO ↓

Do you have an awful auntie?
— YES →
— NO ↓

Are you an owl?
— YES →
— NO ↓

Are you retired?
— NO →
— YES ↓

Do you encourage children to eat lots of sweets?
— NO ↓
— YES →

Does your dad have a really fast car?

Have you ever tried to steal the Crown Jewels?
— YES ↓
— NO →

Do you have a beard?
— YES ↓
— NO →

Are you a newsagent?
— NO ↓
— YES →

MR STINK

AWFUL AUNTIE ALBERTA

DEMON DENTIST

Is your name Raj?
— YES ↓

Have you ever piloted an aeroplane?
— NO →
— YES →

RAJ'S AUNTIE DHRITI

GANGSTA GRANNY

WING COMMANDER BUNTING

RAJ

14

CHARACTER ARE YOU?

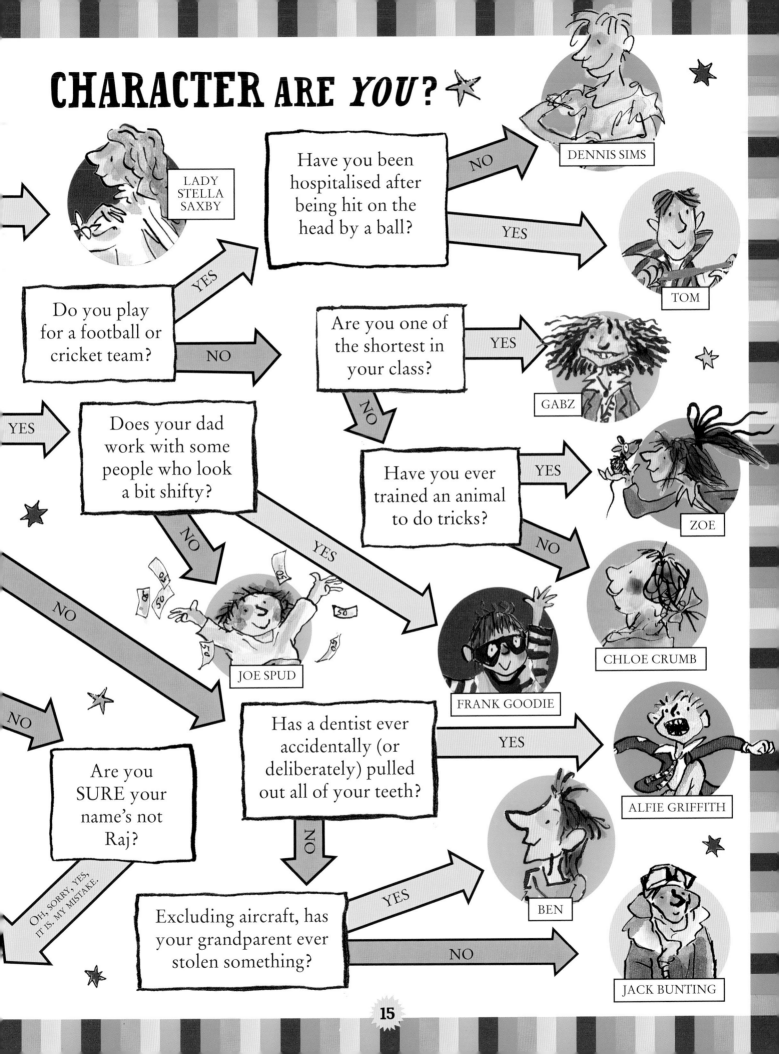

LADY STELLA SAXBY

Have you been hospitalised after being hit on the head by a ball?

NO → DENNIS SIMS

YES → TOM

Do you play for a football or cricket team?

YES

NO →

Are you one of the shortest in your class?

YES → GABZ

NO

Have you ever trained an animal to do tricks?

YES → ZOE

NO → CHLOE CRUMB

Does your dad work with some people who look a bit shifty?

YES

NO →

YES → JOE SPUD

FRANK GOODIE

Are you SURE your name's not Raj?

OH, SORRY, YES, IT IS, MY MISTAKE.

NO

Has a dentist ever accidentally (or deliberately) pulled out all of your teeth?

YES → ALFIE GRIFFITH

NO

Excluding aircraft, has your grandparent ever stolen something?

YES → BEN

NO → JACK BUNTING

RAJ'S DEALS

WELCOME to Raj's Special Offers website. You can buy all my fantastic items online. We also sell cards for every occasion and I mean *every* occasion. Please look around. Although you'll have to COLLECT them in my shop. And PAY for them in my shop. And ORDER them in my shop. Happy online shopping!

ONLY **17** SCHOOL CHILDREN ALLOWED ON THE WEBSITE AT **ONE** TIME.

BANAN

GREETINGS CARDS DO NOT TOUCH! (Touching costs extra.)

EVERY pack of HUNDREDS & THOUSANDS comes with **6 EXTRA** HUNDREDS & THOUSANDS **FREE!** *Count them yourself if you don't believe me!*

SHRIMPS

HAPPY INTERNATIONAL **RAJ DAY!**

To the WORLD'S WORST MUM

I'M SORRY YOU'VE CUT YOUR OWN FRINGE

SORRY YOU GOT A GRAZE ON YOUR BOTTOM WHEN YOU FELL OFF YOUR SKATEBOARD

CONGRATULATIONS ON YOUR **BABY**

Buy a **PENCIL** – get a built-in pencil **LEAD** at **NO EXTRA COST!**

B.O.F.G.O.F.* on FLAKES! *(* Buy one Flake, get one Flake!)*

15% OFF refurbished lollipops *(Lollipops were licked no more than twice.)*

2-4-1 OFFER Buy TWO Curly Wurlys and FOUR Curly Wurlys... and get **ONE FULL PRICE!**

THE BEST DRESSES TO WEAR FOR FOOTBALL

This season's hottest fashions for football have just been announced! Check out the latest high-end designs that are perfect for catwalk and football pitch alike.

L'INCOGNITO

This year's must-have football dress is L'Incognito, designed in the season's hottest colour: football-pitch green. Original, stylish and grassy, this dress will make you not only the envy of Paris Fashion Week, but also nearly invisible in a football match – so you can jump up and tackle opposition players before they even begin to realise you're not just a piece of turf.

DOPPELGÄNGER

Little black dresses never go out of fashion. At first glance, the Doppelgänger is a timeless, simple and elegant design. But the masterstroke of this creation is that it is very, very easily mistaken for a referee's kit. This means you can award your own team lots of penalties while sending off as many opposition players as you like. I know what you're thinking: what if the REAL referee asks you what you're playing at? Simple! Send *him* off as well.

L'EXUBÉRANCE

The needlework on L'Exubérance dress is exquisite in its detail, contrasting the white silk with the delicate embroidery of footballs. But the real secret of this dress is that no one will be able to tell which of the footballs is the real one. Once the other team are completely befuddled, you can run up to the goal and reveal that the REAL football has actually been underneath your dress all along – then kick it into the goal. One-nil!

THE KALEIDOSCOPE

The Kaleidoscope is bold, eye-catching and perfect if you plan on playing for lots of different football teams. It's made from thousands of tiny hand-stitched squares taken from every football kit in the world, ever. So simply by wearing this dress you can be sure you're in the right colours, whatever team you're playing for.
(PLEASE NOTE: do not allow your team to wear the Kaleidoscope if the opposition are also wearing it, otherwise things will get very confusing.)

LE BARRICADE

This dress is elegant, frilly – and, most of all, perfect for goalkeepers. Not only will it give you an air of continental sophistication, it will also make it literally impossible for the other team to score against you.
(PLEASE NOTE: not to be worn on windy days, otherwise you might end up being blown into a neighbouring field or, if it's particularly gusty, to France.)

MRS TRAFE'S COOKERY BOOK RANGE

Hello, I'm Mrs Trafe, everyone's favourite dinner lady from *Billionaire Boy*, and here are some of my worst-selling recipe books so you can eat my disgusting food from the comfort of your own home. I would **never** dream of eating this muck, but you fill your boots.

101 RECIPES WITH BAT-SICK

- ✵ Bat-sick On Toast
- ✵ Bat-sick Under Toast
- ✵ Bat-sick Next to Toast
- ✵ Cold Bat-sick
- ✵ Warm Bat-sick
- ✵ Room-temperature Bat-sick
- ✵ Batsickia Fromaggi (bat-sick pizza with bat-sick cheese and crust stuffed with bat-sick)
- ✵ Bat-sick Dauphinoise
- ✵ Bat-sick Mousse
- ✵ Bat-sicky Toffee Pudding

ARE YOU HAVING A PARTY? DO YOU HATE THROWING PARTIES? DO YOU WANT TO NEVER HAVE ANOTHER PARTY? WELL, YOU CAN MAKE SURE THAT PEOPLE WILL **NEVER** WANT TO COME TO ONE OF YOUR PARTIES AGAIN WITH MY DISGUSTING PARTY-FOOD RECIPES.

MRS TRAFE'S PARTY FOOD

- ✵ Worm and Pineapple on a Stick
- ✵ Bin-juice Punch
- ✵ Blended Toad-spit Dip
- ✵ Fizzy Bathwater Cocktails
- ✵ Vole-dropping Vol-au-vents
- ✵ Used-plaster Dippers
- ✵ Sweet-and-sour Fur Balls
- ✵ Spring Bog Rolls
- ✵ Spicy Mixed Gravel
- ✵ Old Sock Sprinkled with Foot Cheese

BILLIONAIRE BOY

MRS TRAFE'S WOODLAND FEASTS

- Rabbit-dropping Roll
- Badger-poop Pâté
- Twice-battered Leaf Mould
- Sparrow-feather Smoothie
- Twig Twiglets (just twigs)
- Foxtail Soup
- Soil Stew
- Toadstool Trifle
- Maggot Risotto
- Chewed Tennis Ball in a Swan's Wee Sauce

ALWAYS ASK A GROWN-UP TO HELP YOU IN THE KITCHEN

A TASTE OF THE CANAL

WHY GO TO THE TROUBLE OF FISHING IN SEAS AND RIVERS WHEN THERE ARE DELIGHTS TO BE DREDGED FROM YOUR LOCAL CANAL?

- Rusty Shopping Trolley in a Bun
- Stewed Bike Tyre
- Boiled Boot
- Tandoori Traffic Cone
- Duck-poo Crêpes (posh word for pancakes)
- 30-day-aged Fizzy Pop Bottle in an Algae Sauce
- Mattress Drizzle in Extra-virgin Barge Oil
- Nappy Burgers
- Braised Carrier Bag
- Deep-fried Brick

Rabbit-dropping ROLL

RECIPE

INGREDIENTS

15 plain digestive biscuits

15 marshmallows

80g of rabbit droppings (or plain chocolate chips or chunks if you prefer)

175ml of condensed milk, with a little extra just in case

100g of chocolate sprinkles to coat

METHOD

ASK A GROWN-UP TO HELP YOU

- Put the biscuits in a sealed plastic bag, and crush them up with a rolling pin – when crushed up, put them in a large mixing bowl.

- Chop each marshmallow into four pieces and add them to the bowl along with the chocolate chips and condensed milk.

- Mix with a wooden spoon until everything is combined – and sticky! If it's too dry, add a little more condensed milk.

- Spread most of the chocolate sprinkles over a large piece of clingfilm (or foil). Tip the mixture on top of it and shape it into a long sausage – about 30cm long.

- Spread the rest of the chocolate sprinkles on top of your sausage and wrap the clingfilm tightly round it, twisting the ends together.

- Put it in the fridge to chill for four to six hours – then slice and serve your delicious droppings dessert!

BURT & SHEILA'S
DATING AGENCY APPLICATIONS

WILL BURT AND SHEILA FROM *RATBURGER* HAVE A LOVE MATCH? SEE HOW THEIR ANSWERS COMPARE

BURT

RATBURGER

LIKES: Pulverising rats

DISLIKES: Unpulverised rats

FAVOURITE BOOK: Books are bad for you

FAVOURITE FILM: Clingfilm

FAVOURITE MUSIC: Rat screams

FAVOURITE CRISP FLAVOUR: Rat flavour (if not available, then prawn cocktail)

WHEN DID YOU LAST WASH YOUR HAIR? Why would you do that?

OF WHICH FEATURE ARE YOU MOST PROUD? Warts

WHAT DO YOU LOOK FOR IN A WOMAN? Greasy hair

WHERE DO YOU LIVE? My van

FAVOURITE MEAL: Rat droppings from the floor of my van

WHERE DO YOU LIKE TO GO ON HOLIDAY? Back of my van – I like to lie on the grille and get a tan.

FAVOURITE JOKE: Knock, knock. Who's there? No one, it's the sound of me hitting rats.

WHAT IS YOUR WORST HABIT? I'm ashamed to say I sometimes pick my nose and don't eat it. What a waste. You should always eat your bogeys.

PERFECT DATE: Walk to a lovely field, lay down a picnic blanket, light a candle and cook a rat on it.

WHAT'S YOUR IDEA OF HAPPINESS? Other people being unhappy

SHEILA

LIKES: Eating prawn-cocktail crisps

DISLIKES: Eating crisps that aren't prawn-cocktail flavour

FAVOURITE BOOK: Favourite what?

FAVOURITE FILM: The film that forms on a month-old cup of tea – delicious!

FAVOURITE MUSIC: The sound of crisp packets opening

FAVOURITE CRISP FLAVOUR: Prawn cocktail

OF WHICH FEATURE ARE YOU MOST PROUD? Bum boils

WHAT DON'T YOU LOOK FOR IN A MAN? Teeth

WHERE DO YOU LIVE? At home, stupid

FAVOURITE MEAL: Prawn-cocktail crisp bits that have collected at the bottom of the bin

WHERE DO YOU LIKE TO GO ON HOLIDAY? Crisp factory – a fourteen-night tour

FAVOURITE JOKE:
Q) Doctor, doctor – I'm very unhealthy and I smell of prawns.
A) That'll be all the prawn-cocktail crisps you eat! (Actually it's not really a joke, more a conversation I had this morning.)

WHAT IS YOUR WORST HABIT? Sometimes I do a really smelly trump when I'm on my own, rather than do it in someone's face. It's a waste of a really good blow-off.

PERFECT DATE: A romantic bath with rose petals scattered on it – but rose petals are disgusting, so scatter prawn-cocktail crisps instead

WHAT'S YOUR IDEA OF HAPPINESS? There's nothing I like more than bringing misery to my step-daughter, Zoe.

CONGRATULATIONS! SHEILA AND BURT ARE A **99%** LOVE MATCH!

TURN TO PAGE 43 FOR A SUPER MEGA-FUN DATING QUIZ!

BEN'S GUIDE to PRETENDING to do what you're TOLD

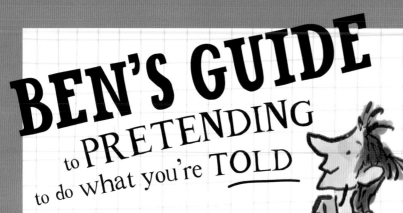

GANGSTA GRANNY

HOW TO PRETEND
You've HAD A BATH

1) Fill the bath for ten minutes, but, whatever you do, DON'T GET IN.
2) Squirt in some of your favourite bubble bath to not wash in.
3) Wet your towel under the taps.
4) Take off your shoes and socks, wipe them on the wet towel and leave wet footprints.
5) Dip your head into the bathtub to make it look like you've washed it.
6) Pull out the plug to send all the hot, clean water down the drain.
7) Breathe on the mirror to make it steam up.
8) With a brown felt-tip pen, draw a scum line round the inside of the bath.

HOW TO PRETEND
You've TIDIED YOUR ROOM

1) Do a three-year degree in fine art and pass with flying colours.
2) Now paint a life-size, super-realistic picture of your bedroom with everything tidied.
3) Wait for the painting to dry.
4) Now hang the painting in the doorway so if your mum or dad opens the door it looks like your bedroom is perfectly tidy.
5) Remember: don't try to walk into the room – it's not your room, it's a large painting.

HOW TO PRETEND
You're ASLEEP

1) Wait until night-time.
2) Put on your pyjamas.
3) Lie in bed under the duvet.
4) Don't move.
5) Close your eyes and keep them closed. (Whatever you do, don't fall asleep.)
6) Keep this up for 8–10 hours.
7) Repeat this the next night.
8) Don't forget to act like you're really awake during the day.

HOW TO PRETEND
You've EATEN YOUR VEGETABLES

1) Find a friendly tortoise.
2) Hide the tortoise in your pocket.
3) When your mum or dad serves up vegetables, wait until their back is turned, then get the tortoise out and let it eat the vegetables while you say the following: "Mmmm. These vegetables are great."
4) Secretly collect any resulting tortoise droppings in a plastic sandwich bag, wait till breaktime at school the next day, then shake them down your trouser leg until they fall on to the playground.
5) This plan doesn't work during the winter months as the tortoise will be hibernating. During this period, use a rabbit.

HOW TO PRETEND
You've GONE TO THE TOILET

1) Lock the toilet door.
2) Fill your mouth from the tap.
3) Gently spray a stream of water from your mouth into the toilet bowl.
4) Flush the toilet.
5) Don't forget to not wash your hands.

You made it! Run complete. Now all you have to do is run back to the changing rooms, which are now two miles away.

55

Your race number's fallen off. Go back to get it.

54

53

52

51

The Grubb twins are throwing mud at you. Take a detour.

50

43

Bob shares his emergency back-up chocolate bar with you. Energy boost!

44

45

46

Stop to catch your breath. Miss a go.

47

48

49

42

41

40

39

38

37

36

29

You slip over and fall down a mudslide (exactly like this one).

30

31

32

Mr Bruise accuses you of cheating and makes you start the lap again.

33

34

35

28

27

Skip a checkpoint.

26

25

24

23

You take a shortcut when PE teacher Mr Bruise isn't looking.

22

15

16

You get a stitch. Back you go!

17

18

19

20

21

14

13

12

11

10

9

8

Flip an arrow and send everyone else the wrong way.

1

2

3

Your friend Bob shares a chocolate bar with you. Energy boost!

4

Trip over your shoelace. Miss a turn.

5

6

7

JOE SPUD'S CROSS-COUNTRY Slides AND Ladders

RULES OF THE RACE

Draw round a penny and cut out the circle. Draw in your face – this is your "runner". Each runner begins at the start line. Take it in turns to roll the dice. Run forward the number of spaces on the dice. If you land on a ladder – go up it! If you find yourself at the top of a mudslide, slide down it! (While that might sound like fun, it's actually a bad thing.) First runner to reach the finish line wins.

BILLIONAIRE BOY

HOW TO MAKE YOUR OWN David Walliams BOOK TITLE

SMELLY CHEF

1) Roll two dice. Use the two numbers you get to create a two-digit number. Use that to select your ADJECTIVE.
2) Roll two dice again. Use the two numbers to create another two-digit number. Use this to select your PERSON.
3) You now have your own Walliams book title.
4) Now simply write your book and wait for it to be adapted into a successful TV show.

ADJECTIVES

11	Silly	34	Farting	56	Slimy
12	Lazy	35	Naughty	61	Wobbly
13	Nutty	36	Spherical	62	Mysterious
14	Flabby	41	Sticky	63	Prehistoric
15	Gangly	42	Smelly	64	Moody
16	Mushy	43	Rotating	65	Teeny-Tiny
21	Boring	44	Naughty	66	Damp
22	Grumpy	45	Bossy		
23	Squishy	46	Hairy		
24	Rapping	51	Muddy		
25	Pooping	52	Stupid		
26	Rancid	53	Greedy		
31	Furry	54	Squeezy		
32	Dopey	55	Pesky		
33	Floppy				

EXAMPLE

6 AND 3 = 63

PREHISTORIC

PERSONS

11 Mum	41 Bus Driver
12 Dad	42 Toilet Attendant
13 Sister	43 Ceiling-tile Installer
14 Brother	44 Talent Show Judge
15 Cousin	45 Chef
16 Second Cousin Twice Removed	46 Fireman
21 Mother-in-Law	51 Teacher
22 Father-in-Law	52 Postman
23 Uncle	53 Duck
24 Auntie	54 Plumber
25 Boyfriend	55 Traffic Warden
26 Girlfriend	56 Squirrel
31 Baby	61 *X Factor* Host
32 Doggie	62 Archaeologist
33 Moggie	63 Santa
34 Doctor	64 Footballer
35 Hairdresser	65 Carrot
36 Astronaut	66 Dinner Lady

FURRY FOOTBALLER

EXAMPLE

5 AND 6 = 56

SQUIRREL

TEENY-TINY TOILET ATTENDANT

PREHISTORIC SQUIRREL

THE NAUGHTY CARROT
Nutty Archaeologist
Farting Father-in-Law
THE BOSSY PLUMBER
STICKY SANTA
THE MYSTERIOUS CEILING-TILE INSTALLER
THE PESKY SISTER
THE SMELLY CHEF
FLABBY AUNTIE
MUSHY MOGGIE
DAMP DAD
The Boring X Factor Host
ROTATING DUCK
THE GREEDY MUM
THE SPHERICAL SECOND COUSIN TWICE REMOVED

HOW TO DRAW LIKE *Tony Ross*

How lucky is David Walliams to have the artistic genius Tony Ross to draw pictures for zillions of his books. Now you've got your title, you are ready to design your own book cover. All you need to do first is master the simple art of drawing like Tony.

1 MAKE A FACE!

TONY TIP: Full lips are harder to draw than a little line.

1) First draw an oval

2) Draw a cross – note the horizontal line for the eye position – then add in two more horizontal lines for the nose and mouth position.

3) Add the ears between the eye and nose line, and draw in eyes, eyebrows and a nose and mouth.

4) Move the lines around to make your face look sideways . . .

5) or down . . .

6) or up!

2 EXPRESSIONS

1) A picture tells a thousand words and so do the expressions on your face!

2) Happiness – add eyebrows and a smiley mouth.

3) Sad – little downward eyebrows and a downturned sad mouth.

4) Angry – frowning eyebrows and a little straight mouth.

5) Frightened – the hair stands on end. Eyes wide open with raised eyebrows and mouth going "ooh!".

TONY TIP: You can also show the shoulders drawn in shaky lines and add some shaky lines around the head.

30

FEATURES

Features are important to give your character personality! Different nose shapes are particularly effective.

TONY TIP: Eyes set wide apart can look innocent; close together can look crafty. Too far either way and your character will look a little dim.

TONY TIP: If you point the nose facing different ways, it looks like the character is looking in different ways.

4 MOVEMENT

Movement is important too. You can work out movement with stick people first then fill them out into real people.

5 CHARACTER

What kind of clothes and special features does your character have?

Crisp white shirt

Flying ace's moustache

Double-breasted blazer

Royal Air Force tie

Service medals

Polished gold buttons

Neatly pressed grey slacks

Slippers

DID YOU KNOW? Sir Quentin Blake illustrated *The Boy in the Dress* and *Mr Stink*!

HOW TO DESIGN YOUR OWN BOOK COVER

Ever heard the phrase "don't judge a book by its cover"? Well, ignore it. Nobody wants to read a book that looks boring, so here's how to make yours look brilliant!

TITLE

FRONT COVER

TOP TIP
Don't forget to write your name as the author. But, if your book's rubbish, put someone else's name on the cover.

TITLE AND STRAPLINE

Turn to page 28 for some great title ideas! If you want yours to be longer, maybe you should split it in two: a title and a strapline – an extra line that "sells" the story and makes the reader want to find out more… Think about the lettering you're going to use too. Should it look messy or neat? Handwritten or formal? 3D or flat?

Typewriter   Poshley Manor

CHUNKY   Notebook

Disco   Whirly and Curly

CIRCUS

ILLUSTRATION

Here's your chance to shine! Decide on your front cover picture. Which characters will it show? What will they be doing? Is it a scene, or a border round the title? Practise a couple of times in rough first.

TOP TIP
Better give yourself the credit for being the publisher too – don't forget to draw a cracking logo for the spine.

David Walliams

FREE MINI inside*

BAD DAD

David Walliams

FREE HOSPITAL DINNER INSIDE

THE MIDNIGHT GANG

BLURB

The blurb on the back will make people decide whether they want to read your story, so make it mysterious and intriguing BUT DON'T GIVE THE ENDING AWAY! Remember to add the price (a million pounds is reasonable), a barcode and maybe another illustration or two.

BACK COVER

DRAW A NEW
David Walliams COVER

Hi,

I'm David Walliams' publisher, Paige Turner. David keeps writing books faster than we can publish them and I wish he would stop, but he won't. So I need someone to draw a cover for each of David's novels that I haven't got round to publishing yet. I've listed the books below. Have fun drawing them!

    Many thanks,

Paige Turner

MR SHRINK
A girl called Chloe finds a tiny, filthy man who smells (although not THAT much because he's really small). When it looks like he might be driven out of town, Chloe hides him in a matchbox.

HATBURGER
Burger-seller Burt secretly makes burgers out of hats. A young girl, Zoe, finds a very talented hat that can dance really well. Can she stop Burt from turning her dancing hat into a hatburger?

THE DOG IN THE DRESS
The tale of a bulldog that likes wearing dresses, but is shunned by all the other dogs in his litter for doing so.

BILLIONAIRE BEAR
Rory is a bear whose dad is a billionaire (and a bear). Rory decides to go to the local comprehensive school, where he makes friends and also eats the teachers.

DEMON FLORIST
An evil florist comes to town and steals flowers and replaces them with ugly weeds.

HAMSTER GRANNY
By day Ben's gran is a boring old lady - by night she's a hamster. Together, Ben and his gran try to steal the Queen's nuts.

WAFFLE AUNTIE
Aunt Alberta traps her niece in Saxby Hall and attempts to steal her inheritance. Oh wait, did I mention she's made entirely of waffles?

GRANDPA'S GREATEST CAPE
A very short book about an old man who just has a really fancy cape.

BAT DAD
Frank finds out that his dad is actually Batman. But will the evil crime boss Mr Big stop him saving people's lives? No. Because he's Batman.

THE BIG KNIGHT GANG
Midnight is the time when all the knights are fast asleep, except of course... the Big Knight Gang. These giant knights get up to have secret adventures! (But they're not very secret because they wear noisy armour and they keep bashing their heads on beams.)

HOW TO BLING YOUR GRANNY'S RIDE

IS YOUR GRANNY A GANGSTA? DOES YOUR GRANNY HAVE A MOBILITY SCOOTER THAT NEEDS JAZZING UP? HERE ARE SOME TIPS ON HOW TO MAKE HER SCOOTER A SUPER-DUPER SCOOTER...

Motorbike handlebars

In-basket sound system (plays hymns at 1,000 decibels)

Framed photo of Prince Charles in his swimming trunks

GET SOME PLAIN WHITE PAPER AND DRAW YOUR OWN IDEAS!

Souped-up lawnmower engine (max speed 12 mph)

Retractable knitting needles in wheels (for taking out other scooters in the post-office queue)

THE MIDNIGHT GANG
FILES

TOP SECRET

THESE SECRET FILES ARE ONLY TO BE READ
BY MEMBERS OF THE MIDNIGHT GANG. THESE
FILES WERE COMPILED BY ME, THE PORTER. IF
YOU ARE NOT IN THE MIDNIGHT GANG,
DO NOT READ ON.

I MEAN IT!

PORTER

Are you still reading? Well then, you must be part of the
Midnight Gang. You must NEVER tell anyone about
what you read on these pages. EVER!

I started the Midnight Gang fifty years ago. I came to
the Lord Funt Hospital as a baby, and, because I needed
operation after operation, I never got to leave. I could only watch out of the
window as all the other children trotted off to school. I remember thinking, "Why
should they have all the fun?" I loved to read fairy stories – my dream was to be
a handsome prince. And one night my dream came true! It was the most magical
night of my life. Somewhere deep in my heart I will never forget the incredible
feeling of being whoever I wanted to be.

Since then, the Midnight Gang has made thousands of children's dreams come
true. Here are some of the most daring ones of all.

YEAR: 1969	NAME: SANDY PLANK
INJURY: FOOD POISONING	DREAM: TRAVEL TO THE MOON

HOW HER DREAM CAME TRUE:

I GRABBED THE EMPTY FISH BOWL FROM RECEPTION AND PLACED IT ON SANDY'S HEAD. SANDY WAS THEN PUT IN A ROCKET (THAT I MADE OUT OF CARDBOARD), PLACED IN THE LIFT AND LAUNCHED TO THE MOON (ALSO KNOWN AS THE 44TH FLOOR). A 100% REALISTIC LUNAR SURFACE WAS CREATED BY COLLECTING THE GRAVEL FROM ALL THE HOSPITAL'S POT PLANTS AND SCATTERING IT OVER THE CORRIDOR FLOOR. (IT TOOK ME SIX MONTHS TO PUT ALL THE GRAVEL BACK IN THE PLANT POTS.)

	NAME: MARGARET SMITH
YEAR: 1976	DREAM: WIN AN OLYMPIC GOLD MEDAL
INJURY: TWO BROKEN ARMS	

HOW HER DREAM CAME TRUE:

THE CHILDREN MARKED UP A ONE-METRE RUNNING RACETRACK USING SURGICAL TAPE. THE WINNER, MARGARET, RECEIVED A GOLD MEDAL THAT WAS MADE FROM AN OLD BANDAGE AND A PAINTED BATH PLUG. IT WASN'T QUITE THE OLYMPICS, BUT IT MADE MARGARET SMILE.

YEAR: 1983	NAME: MIKE TEMPLE
INJURY: BURNS ON HIS HAND	DREAM: RIDE A ROLLERCOASTER

HOW HIS DREAM CAME TRUE:

I STRAPPED MIKE TO A HOSPITAL TROLLEY USING A SERIES OF STETHOSCOPES AND SENT IT CAREERING DOWN THE HOSPITAL'S BACK STAIRS AT BREAKNECK (THANKFULLY NOT LITERALLY) SPEED. I MUST SAY, HE WAS BRAVER THAN ME! I ONCE SAT ON THE POSTMAN PAT RIDE IN THE HOSPITAL FOYER AND HAD TO GO LIE DOWN.

YEAR: 2003

INJURY: UNCONTROLLABLE WIND

NAME: LILY HAMMERS

DREAM: BE A POP STAR

HOW HER DREAM CAME TRUE:

I CREATED A STAGE BY PUSHING THREE HOSPITAL BEDS TOGETHER. LILY CLIMBED ON IT AND SANG INTO HER MICROPHONE (AN UPSIDE-DOWN CRUTCH) AS SHE DANCED IN THE SPOTLIGHT (A LAMP "BORROWED" FROM THE OPERATING THEATRE). ALL THE OTHER YOUNG PATIENTS STOOD AND SCREAMED LIKE CRAZED FANS — BUT THEY HAD TO SCREAM VERY QUIETLY AS IT WAS MIDNIGHT. I LOVED THE SINGING, BUT SOME CHILDREN DID PUT COTTON WOOL IN THEIR EARS BECAUSE THEY SAID LILY SOUNDED LIKE A SEAL.

YEAR: 1971

INJURY: GANGRENOUS ARM

NAME: BOB GLIMP

DREAM: BE A TOP PHOTOGRAPHER

HOW HIS DREAM CAME TRUE:

ALL THE KIDS ON THE WARD PRETENDED TO BE MODELS AND WORE A SELECTION OF OUTFITS — ALTHOUGH, ADMITTEDLY, THE OUTFITS WERE MAINLY JUST DIFFERENT-SIZED HOSPITAL GOWNS. BOB THEN TOOK SOME AMAZING, INCREDIBLE IMAGES WITH HIS STATE-OF-THE-ART CAMERA — AN X-RAY MACHINE THAT I SWIPED FROM THE FOURTH FLOOR (AND WHICH, UNFORTUNATELY, TOOK PICTURES OF PEOPLE'S INSIDES, BUT BOB WAS HAPPY ENOUGH).

YEAR: 1971

INJURY: HEAD STUCK IN SAUCEPAN

NAME: DAISY PHILLPOTT

DREAM: BECOME A BALLROOM-DANCE CHAMPION

HOW HER DREAM CAME TRUE:

I CREATED A DANCE FLOOR BY PUSHING ALL THE CHAIRS AND TABLES TO ONE SIDE IN THE CANTEEN. DAISY AND THE OTHER CHILDREN'S DANCE PARTNERS WERE THE SKELETONS FROM THE DOCTOR'S OFFICE. TO MAKE SURE THE SKELETONS STAYED IN TIME WITH THEIR PARTNERS, THEIR BONY TOES WERE SELLOTAPED TO THE CHILDREN'S FEET. LIKE ALL THE BEST MIDNIGHT GANG ADVENTURES, IT WAS BOTH BONKERS AND BRILLIANT.

YEAR: 2013

INJURY: BANDAGED HEAD

NAME: JENNY CARAVAN

DREAM: WIN WIMBLEDON

HOW HER DREAM CAME TRUE:

I CREATED A NET BY TIPPING A BED ON ITS SIDE. BEDPANS WERE USED AS RACKETS (WASHED — OBVIOUSLY!) AND A SPONGE WAS USED AS THE TENNIS BALL. JENNY WON IN AN EPIC FIVE-SET BATTLE AND WAS AWARDED THE COVETED HOSPITAL DINNER PLATE WRAPPED IN TINFOIL. SO, MUCH BETTER THAN THE REAL WIMBLEDON, BECAUSE IT WASN'T CALLED OFF BECAUSE OF RAIN AND YOU DIDN'T HAVE TO PAY EXTORTIONATE AMOUNTS OF MONEY FOR STRAWBERRIES AND CREAM.

YEAR: 1999

INJURY: BROKEN ANKLE

NAME: CHRISTINA WOOFF

DREAM: BE THE FIRST CHILD TO SAIL ROUND THE WORLD

HOW HER DREAM CAME TRUE:

I PULLED CHRISTINA AROUND THE WARD IN A BATHTUB WHILE THE OTHER KIDS THREW CUPS OF WARM WATER AT HER. ONE YOUNG PATIENT EVEN DRESSED AS A SHARK — COMPLETE WITH A CLIPBOARD FIN. FOR ADDED OCEAN REALISM, LIQUID SOAP FROM THE SOAP DISPENSER WAS OCCASIONALLY DROPPED ON CHRISTINA TO SIMULATE SEAGULL DROPPINGS. SHE SMASHED THE WORLD RECORD OF 42 DAYS, COMPLETING HER CIRCUMNAVIGATION IN JUST 27 MINUTES.

YEAR: 2006

INJURY: BOTH ARMS IN SLINGS

NAME: KEVIN SPROTT

DREAM: HAVE A MEDIEVAL JOUST

HOW HIS DREAM CAME TRUE:

KEVIN CLIMBED ON THE BACK OF A FELLOW PATIENT. I GAVE HIM A BUCKET FOR A HELMET AND A MOP TO USE AS A LANCE. THE OTHER CHILD JOUSTING WAS ACCIDENTALLY A LITTLE BIT INJURED AND NEEDED TO GO TO HOSPITAL AFTERWARDS, BUT THAT WAS OK BECAUSE HE WAS ALREADY IN ONE.

Now that you have seen these classified files from the Midnight Gang, you must speak of them to no one. Do whatever you must to ensure that no grown-ups ever read these pages. Although don't go as far as ripping them up and eating them, because otherwise you might end up in the Lord Funt Hospital yourself.

And please, whatever you do, whoever you are, wherever you are... never stop dreaming! No one can take your dreams away from you.

41

AUNTIE FLIP'S
POETRY CORNER

BAD DAD

VOLUME 1

GOOD EVENING.

I'm Flip Goodie, librarian by day and poet also by day (when I'm supposed to be a librarian). I have published hundreds of volumes of my poetry. From my vast body of work I have chosen these, my very best poems, for your delightment.

101 POEMS ABOUT CARAVANNING HOLIDAYS

THINGS I FOUND BETWEEN MY TOES

THE JOYS OF CLOTTED CREAM

Dandelions, Dandelions, Dandelions and More Dandelions

CAR BONNET SONNETS

The Beauty of Jumble Sales

Pressed Flowers and Other Accidental Crushings

THE PLACES I'VE FOUND MY KEYS

FUDGE VOLUMES ONE & TWO

ODE TO A ROAD

We all thank you, Mistress Road,
For taking us to where we want to go-ed.
You take us to the shops and back,
Where I could buy a Caramac.

You take us to the doctor's.
Or to see a friend,
On a weekend,
Who lives round a bend.

Unless you are a toad.
Then you must avoid the road,
For fear of getting mowed
Down. By a car or a truck,
And be reduced to muck.

There are so many roads on which we travel,
Some made of tarmac, others made of gravel.

The A39 is very fine.
The B215 is one I like to drive.
The A377 doesn't go to heaven – it actually goes
    to Devon.
The B1672 is not good if you need to do a poo.
There's no service station at which to stop
    should you need to go plop-plop.

LOZENGE

Oh, lozenge,
Small, and sometimes orange.
Though often blackcurrant,
But nothing rhymes with blackcurrant.

You soothe my throat,
You keep my spirits afloat,
Like a boat. Afloat. On a moat.
Near a goat, eating an oat,
Watching *Murder, She Wrote*.

THE BURT & SHEILA RATBURGER QUIZ!

Burt and Sheila from *Ratburger* were destined to be together. But can you remember how they described themselves in their Dating Agency profiles?

1. *What did Burt say is his favourite book?*
A) *The Vegan Diet Cookbook*
B) *War and Peace* by Leo Tolstoy
C) None – books are bad for you

2. *What does Burt include in his "likes"?*
A) Chasing otters
B) Pulverising rats
C) Catching squirrels

3. *What does Burt class as his worst habit?*
A) Accidentally using a fish fork to eat a starter
B) Occasionally forgetting to have a breath mint after a meal
C) Picking his nose and NOT eating it (it's a waste of a good bogey)

4. *What is Burt's favourite film?*
A) *My Little Pony: The Movie*
B) *Ratatouille*
C) Clingfilm (because it seals in that mouldy goodness)

5. *Of which feature is Burt most proud?*
A) His carefully plucked eyebrows
B) His warts
C) His six-pack

6. *What does Sheila like listening to most?*
A) Calming classical concertos
B) Beautiful panpipe music
C) The sound of crisp packets opening

7. *What doesn't Sheila look for in a man?*
A) Tattoos
B) Hairy knuckles
C) Teeth

8. *What is Sheila's idea of a perfect holiday?*
A) A fourteen-night tour of a crisp factory
B) A yoga retreat in Goa
C) A weekend in a yurt

9. *What is Sheila's favourite film?*
A) *Ice Age 3*
B) *Ice Age 4*
C) The film that forms on a month-old cup of tea

10. *What is Sheila's favourite crisp flavour?*
A) Free-range fairtrade sea salt & organic balsamic vinaigrette
B) Mature vegan cheddar and caramelised shallots
C) Prawn cocktail

ANSWERS ON PAGE 76

BURT
SHEILA
RATBURGER

AROUND THE WORLD IN MR STINK'S BEARD

The stinkiest part of Mr Stink is his beard. It's never been shampooed and has never been in contact with water (except rain and the odd muddy puddle). Here are some of the items from all over the globe that have somehow found their way into his matted mess of chin hair.

VUVUZELA

A legendary plastic South African instrument. Be warned! Should anyone be brave enough to remove this item from Mr Stink's beard and blow into it, it would be REALLY, REALLY annoying.

TUTANKHAMUN'S TOOTHBRUSH

Egyptian-made with solid gold bristles, which are very expensive and shiny, but utterly useless for cleaning teeth.

ROMAN COIN

Dating from the fourth century BC, this specific coin was spent by an ancient Roman schoolchild on an ancient Roman Curly Wurly.

SUSHI ROLL

A Japanese raw-fish delicacy. This particular roll is twelve years old, so is a mere eleven years, three-hundred and sixty four days past its use-by date. That wouldn't put Mr Stink off eating it, though.

QUEEN VICTORIA'S FRONT-DOOR KEY

Who knows how this got in there? For years Vicky had to ring the doorbell so Prince Albert would let her in, because she was famously too lazy to go to the key cutters and get another one.

THE KOH-I-NOOR DIAMOND

Unearthed in India, this is the world's most expensive diamond. (Although it could also just be an old Christmas decoration.)

BABY GRIZZLY BEAR

This Canadian animal appears to be stuck to Mr Stink's beard with maple syrup, but is very difficult to see because Mr Stink's beard actually closely resembles a grizzly bear.

TINY ICEBERG

This iceberg fragment is from the North Pole. It remains frozen in the coldest region of Mr Stink's beard – under his chin.

A £5 WOOLWORTHS VOUCHER

Archaeologists believe this extremely ancient artefact originated from the Abingdon shopping precinct.

BOOMERANG

No Australian boomerang is coming back once it's found its way into the bristly maze of Mr Stink's beard.

AUNTIE ALBERTA'S OWLEUM

Here are the plans for Auntie Alberta's Owl Museum, or "Owleum". Inside, you will find various incredibly rare breeds of owl immortalised forever.

CHAMELEON OWL: ABLE TO DISGUISE ITSELF TO BLEND IN TO ANY SITUATION

THE VERY-SMALL-WINGED OWL: NESTS HIGH UP ON CLIFFS; LIFE EXPECTANCY OF EIGHT SECONDS

AUSTRALIAN OWL

RICHARD OWL: NOT AN OWL, BUT A MAN WHOSE SURNAME HAPPENED TO BE OWL

UNDERWATER OWL

A COLLECTION OF RARE STUFFED OWLS

TYRANNOROWLUS REX: THE EARLIEST-KNOWN OWL

ENTRANCE

KNIGHT OWL

PUFFER OWL: INFLATES TO THE SIZE OF A BEACH BALL WHEN THREATENED

SPOTTED OWL

LESSER-SPOTTED OWL

TRANSYLVANIAN VAMPIRE OWL: ONLY COMES OUT IN THE DAYTIME

MOON OWL: ONLY FOUND IN THE CRATERS OF THE EARTH'S MOON

MICRO OWL: THE WORLD'S SMALLEST OWL, AT ONLY 1MM TALL

MERM-OWL: HALF OWL, HALF FISH

JET-PROPELLED OWL: THIS OWL FLIES SOLELY BY USING THE POWER OF ITS OWN TRUMPS

BARN OWL: NAMED AFTER ITS DISTINCTIVE BARN SHAPE

BABY-OWL EXPERIENCE:
YOU DRESS UP AS A BABY OWL AND A CLOCKWORK MOTHER OWL FEEDS YOU REGURGITATED WORMS AND MOUSE HEADS

OWLEUM GIFT SHOP,
WHERE YOU CAN BUY ITEMS INCLUDING...

- Tea Towl – an owl whose feathers you can use to dry the dishes
- Beach Towl – a larger owl whose feathers you can use to dry yourself on the beach
- Stuff-your-own-owl kit (owl not included)
- Guess Whoo? – the owl board game
- Scented pencil toppers (smells of owl droppings)
- "World's Best Owl" mug – a fun gift for your nearest and dearest owl
- Model Owleum – a perfect miniature replica of the Owleum (it's so accurate that it even has a tiny gift shop inside with an even smaller model Owleum in, and so on).
- Owl sandals – ideal for when you take your owl to the beach
- A *101 Relaxing Owl Screeches* CD
- Owl repellent – for people who don't like owls
- Owl wings – fly like an owl!*
  (* Not suitable for flying)

Study the Owleum for 60 seconds, then turn the page to take on THE OWLEUM MEMORY CHALLENGE!

THE WAGNER EXHIBITION

A room dedicated to the memory of my favourite owl, Wagner.

OIL PAINTINGS I PAINTED OF WAGNER AS SOME OF MY FAVOURITE HISTORICAL CHARACTERS

BOUDICCA, BRITON WHO BATTLED THE ROMANS

ENGLAND'S MOST FAMOUS KING, KING HENRY VIII

RASPUTIN, THE MAD MONK OF RUSSIA

EXIT

AWFUL AUNTIE

AUNTIE ALBERTA'S OWLEUM MEMORY CHALLENGE

A challenge for two players!

RULES

Take it in turns to answer these questions. The player with the fewest correct answers must pick a forfeit. If it's a draw, you must both pick a forfeit.

QUESTIONS FOR PLAYER ONE

1. The world's smallest owl is 10mm tall. True or False?
2. Does the Owleum contain a painting of Wagner dressed as King Henry VII or King Henry VIII?
3. What is the life expectancy of the Very-small-winged Owl – eight seconds or eight minutes?

QUESTIONS FOR PLAYER TWO

1. How tall is the Micro Owl – 1mm or 1m?
2. Is the earliest-known owl called the *Velociraptowl* or the *Tyrannorowlus rex*?
3. On the CD on sale in the gift shop, how many relaxing owl screeches are there – 1,001 or 101?

FORFEITS

Check the answers on page 76. The loser(s) must now pick one of the following forfeits:

★ Run up to an unsuspecting member of your family and shout "Twit-twoo!" at them for thirty seconds.

★ Do ten owl jumps (which are star jumps where you have to flap your arms like an owl).

★ Walk around for ten minutes with a (clean!) pair of pants on your head, saying, "Look at me! I'm the Pants Owl!"

RAJ'S PUZZLE PAGE

Hello – it's Raj here, your trusty newsagent. While I'm famous for my discounted confectionery (current deal: all lollipops come with a complimentary stick!), I also have a wide collection of puzzle magazines. I like to try the puzzles myself sometimes. Which reminds me of another special offer: because I've done the work for you, all magazines with half-completed puzzles are double the price! Overall, I find word searches are usually very hard, so to make them fun I've invented the easiest word search in the world.

ENJOY!

RAJ'S EASIEST WORD SEARCH IN THE WORLD

R	A	J	R	A	J	R	A	J	R
R	A	J	R	A	J	R	A	J	A
R	A	J	R	A	J	R	A	J	J
R	A	J	R	A	J	R	A	J	R
R	A	J	R	A	J	R	A	J	A
R	R	A	J	R	A	J	R	A	J
R	A	J	R	A	J	R	A	J	R
R	A	J	R	A	J	R	A	J	A
A	R	A	J	R	A	J	R	A	J
R	A	J	R	A	J	R	A	J	R

BAD DAD

AUNTIE FLIP'S POETRY CORNER

VOLUME 2

SOME LINES ON *THE ANTIQUES ROADSHOW*

"Hello. I'm a man.
My name is Stan,
From Cheltenham.
I'm standing here with my old bedpan.

Tell me, please – I'm on my knees –
Inside this bedpan, who did wees?"

"I'll look into it for ya...
It was Queen Victoria!"
Said the antiques expert with some
euphoria.

"Did she plop?"
The expert's face did drop.
"Of course she did not –
She's the Queen, you clot."

"Please tell me, shall you,
What is its value?"

"A million pounds," he said with glee.
Stan threw it in the air, celebratory.

"Huzzah! Hooray!" Stan's joy increases,
Until it smashed on the floor in a million
pieces.

"How much now? Is it
still worth any?"
"No. Upon this pan,
no one will spend a
penny."

BUTTON BOX

I put a button in a box.
What I don't put in is socks, or a fox,
or some clocks,
Because they're not buttons.
And this is a button box.
Besides, they wouldn't fit –
And that's the end of it.

BELLY-BUTTON FLUFF

From whence doth thou appear, belly-button
fluff?
And from what are thou made: is it just fluff
and stuff?
I pluck, I sniff, I hold you, I kiss you,
And after a bath I really, really miss you.

My navel fills up like a little fluff binny,
Probably because I have an innie.
But the question I wish to get up and shouty
Is: do you get fluff if you have an outie?

POEM ABOUT A POEM

It's not easy writing a poem,
Even when the rhymes are flowin'.
Cos every line has to rhyme,
Nearly all of the time.

The poem must have a meaning
That the reader can be gleaning.
It could be about anything you choose –
Cats, hairdryers, even a Thomson's cruise.

Don't make it too short.
The end.

THE ANNOYING BROTHER AND SISTER TEST

Hello, I'm Dennis. Like many of you, I have an annoying brother. Mine's called John and his favourite hobby is farting in my face. In fact, it's not just his hobby – it's his passion. I think John might be the most annoying brother in the world, but here's a test you can use to find out exactly how annoying YOUR brother or sister is.

QUESTION ONE:

How often does your brother or sister fart in your face?

A) My brother or sister never guffs.

B) They do between one and five face-farts per day.

C) They guff so often that I've forgotten what fresh air smells like.

D) I don't have a brother or sister; I'm an only child.

QUESTION TWO:

What does your brother or sister do with their bogeys?

A) As far as I'm aware, my brother or sister has never had bogeys.

B) They occasionally flick them at me.

C) They wipe them in my hair in a public space, then they point at me and yell, "Look! It's the Incredible Hulk!"

D) I don't have a brother or sister; I'm an only child.

QUESTION THREE:

Which of your belongings has your brother or sister broken?

A) My brother or sister has never damaged any of my things. In fact, they often tidy up my things and repair any damaged items.

B) They've broken one of my toys.

C) My brother or sister has broken ALL of my toys, and also one of my bones. Then, after I got home from the hospital, they ripped up the X-ray.

D) I don't have a brother or sister; I'm an only child.

QUESTION FOUR:

What does your brother or sister share with you?

A) Everything. They also happily hand over any of their possessions that I want, and let me keep them forever.

B) They once had a packet of Smarties and one Smartie fell on the floor. They let me eat that floor-Smartie, which is technically sharing.

C) Diseases and viruses, which they do by deliberately coughing and sneezing into my mouth.

D) I don't have a brother or sister; I'm an only child.

QUESTION FIVE:

What does your brother or sister do when you do something naughty?

A) Nothing, because they want me to express myself in whatever way I choose.

B) They tell my mum or dad before I've even had a chance to shout, "Don't tell Mum or Da—!"

C) They fart in my face, wipe bogeys in my hair, break my toys (and a bone, and then rip up the X-ray), sneeze into my mouth and THEN tell my mum or dad.

D) My brother or sister doesn't exist because I'm an only child.

MOSTLY As Your brother or sister appears not to be annoying in the slightest. They are perfect in every way. But, by being perfect, they are making you look like a terrible brother or sister, which is actually EXTREMELY ANNOYING.

MOSTLY Bs Your brother or sister is as annoying as most people's brothers or sisters. Which means that when you complain about your annoying brother or sister, sadly no one will give you any sympathy whatsoever. Which is EXTREMELY ANNOYING.

MOSTLY Cs It is a definite, scientific, clinically proven, undeniable fact that your brother or sister is EXTREMELY ANNOYING.

MOSTLY Ds Given your answers, there's a tiny possibility that you might be an only child. To check for sure, look around your house for either brothers or sisters. If there aren't any, then it's increasingly likely that you ARE an only child. The good news is: you don't have a brother or sister to annoy you! The bad news is: when you do something naughty, you haven't got anyone else on whom to blame it. Which is EXTREMELY ANNOYING.

THE **100%** NON-SCIENTIFIC ANNOYING BROTHER OR SISTER TEST

MUMMY'S TOOTH-CARE RANGE

BECAUSE MUMMY WANTS TEETH JUST LIKE YOURS

"Let me introduce myself. I am your new dentist. My name is Miss Root, but I ask all my little patients like you to call me 'Mummy'."

MUMMY PROMISES THAT HER

EXTRA-SENSITIVE TOOTHPASTE

will make your teeth extra sensitive, so that even lukewarm water will send shockwaves of pain through your teeth and deep into your gums.

MUMMY'S EXTRA-SENSITIVE

MUMMY'S TRIPLE STRIPE

EVERY TUBE OF

MUMMY'S TRIPLE STRIPE

toothpaste has three action stripes running right the way through it. The red stripe is strawberry cheesecake, the blue stripe is raspberry sherbert while the white stripe is 100% plaque. Guaranteed to transform your smile in days.

MUMMY'S NEW FORMULA has the minty freshness of mint and the coally blackness of coal. Use

TEETH-BLACKENING FORMULA

twice a day, and Mummy guarantees people will stop dead in their tracks to stare at your eye-catching smile.

MUMMY'S TEETH-BLACKENING

52

SWILL MUMMY'S SWEETENED MOUTHWASH

around your beautiful teeth at least six times a day, and you'll quickly see the remarkable difference.

MAX COLA FLAVOUR

CHOCOLATE FUDGE BROWNIE FLAVOUR

LEMON MERINGUE PIE FLAVOUR

MUMMY'S CANDYFLOSS DENTAL FLOSS

Reaches all the parts of your precious gnashers that Mummy's toothpaste couldn't quite reach. Enjoy the 100% real sugar taste of candyfloss. Because it is made of candyfloss.

MUMMY'S CANDYFLOSS DENTAL FLOSS

MUMMY'S TURBO ELECTRIC TOOTHBRUSH

The Turbo Mummy-B electric toothbrush removes plaque, and anything else that gets in its way – including teeth. Mummy promises that if you switch to the Turbo Mummy-B, with its industrial-strength steel bristles, you soon won't have to worry about your teeth ever again.

MUMMY'S POPPING-CANDY BRACES

Get your teeth into line with Mummy's popping-candy dental braces. Mummy insists that you wear them twenty-four hours a day, seven days a week, whether your teeth need straightening or not.

THE OFFICIAL GUIDE TO YOUR SPITFIRE

DRIVING TEST

L

⭐ **DO** make sure there is enough room for your Spitfire to get out of the Imperial War Museum.

⭐ **DON'T** try to drive your Spitfire through the fire exit. The wings will fall off. And it's very hard to fly a plane with no wings.

⭐ **DO** make sure your Spitfire is full of fuel, so stop off at the local garage to fill up. Try to use unleaded petrol as it's better for the environment.

NO EXIT

⭐ **DON'T** forget your wallet, because you'll need to pay for the petrol, which will be pricey because you are in a Spitfire.

⭐ **DO** drive in the centre of the road. Otherwise you might knock the wings off. As I've said before – you do need wings. Two are preferable, but you need one as a minimum.

DON'T drive in the bus lanes. You might get a fine. And bus drivers tend to get very irate, especially if you're driving a Spitfire.

DO stop at a red light.

DON'T stop at a red light if the police are chasing you. Just drive on through.

DO find a long stretch of road if you wish to take off.

DON'T try to take off from somebody's driveway. There's a very good chance you will not become airborne.

DO bring snacks with you. You may get peckish. Scotch eggs, pork pies, scones, boiled sweets, Victoria sponge cakes…

DOUGHNUT is another snack you might like to take.

DON'T try to consume liquids while you're flying. Remember this handy rhyme: "If you're doing a loop-the-loop, don't eat soup."

DO bring a gramophone and records that you can play as you fly, including pop hits like "Rule, Britannia!", "Pomp and Circumstance" and "Land of Hope and Glory".

DON'T try to play the piano as it may obstruct your vision, and also make it difficult to take off.

DO shout, "Up, up and away!" when you finally become airborne.

DON'T shout, "Bananas, bananas, bananas!" Otherwise people will think you've gone bananas. Or that you're selling bananas. Or that you've gone bananas and are selling bananas – which would be, in a word, bananas.

DO use the parachute if you need to bail out in an emergency.

DON'T use a pair of your old Y-fronts. No one wants to see them and they are unlikely to slow your descent.

Finally, **DO** try to learn all about landing *before* you take off or you'll find yourself in a bit of a pickle.

DANGER!

KEY STAGE 27 in the world of David Walliams Studies Advanced Level: Unit 1

Time: 2 hours Ref WODW01/01

This is the exam paper for your David Walliams Studies module. You have two hours to complete it. During the exam you must remain absolutely silent. When I say, "Begin," you must turn this paper over, and then turn it back because the questions are on this side. Begin!

Full Name:

You must have:
A calculator, a pencil, a rubber, a brain and ideally an encyclopaedic knowledge of the world of David Walliams.

Q1
How many hamsters has David Walliams killed off?

- ○ **A** None
- ○ **B** One
- ○ **C** Four or more

Q2
What make of car is Queenie in _Bad Dad_?

- ○ **A** An ice-cream van
- ○ **B** Mini
- ○ **C** Reliant Robin

Q3
Which of these has poisoned the largest number of schoolchildren?

- ○ **A** Burt's burgers
- ○ **B** Mrs Trafe's school dinners
- ○ **C** David Walliams' farts

Q4
Who – or what – is Bum Air?

- ○ **A** Raj's nickname for some out-of-date baked beans he's trying to flog in _Awful Auntie_
- ○ **B** Len Spud's airline in _Billionaire Boy_
- ○ **C** David Walliams' childhood nickname

Q5
What's the longest word to appear in any of David's books?

- ○ **A** A long "burp!" in _Mr Stink_
- ○ **B** A long "ah!" in _Demon Dentist_
- ○ **C** A long "haha!" in _The Boy in the Dress_

Q6
Which of these wild claims was NOT made on the front cover of a David Walliams book?

- ○ **A** Free billion-pound note inside!
- ○ **B** Free Crown Jewel inside!
- ○ **C** Free Spitfire included!

Q7

Which of these locations has NOT featured in a David Walliams book?

- ◯ **A** The Axe & Executioner pub
- ◯ **B** Raj's Nail Salon
- ◯ **C** Twilight Towers old people's home

Q8

What was the first book that David Walliams wrote?

- ◯ **A** *The Boy in the Dress*
- ◯ **B** *Mr Stink*
- ◯ **C** *Harry Potter and the Philosopher's Stone*

Q9

Which of these characters has NOT featured in a David Walliams book?

- ◯ **A** Oddmund Oddmund
- ◯ **B** Nurse Nincompoop
- ◯ **C** Sir Dirk Doddery

Q10

David Walliams wrote his first children's novel in 2008 and has released one every year since. If he lives to the year 2107 (when he'll be 136 years old) and continues to write a new book every year, including that year, how many books will he have written in total?

- ◯ **A** 99 books
- ◯ **B** 100 books
- ◯ **C** 2,107 books

Pens down!

The exam is over.
You have now completed your exam. Please mark your own papers.

-1 POINT – GRADE F

You can't possibly have -1 point. You must have added your score up incorrectly, and as such I am also failing you at GCSE Maths.

0–2 POINTS – GRADE E

You should be ashamed of yourself. Immediately buy every single one of David's books again and read them from cover to cover.

3–4 POINTS – GRADE D

At this rate there's no way you'll be allowed to take the David Walliams A-level.

5–6 POINTS – GRADE C

Not bad! Although not really that good either.

7–8 POINTS – GRADE B

You're smarter than you look. Well done!

9–10 POINTS – GRADE A

Congratulations! That's a highly respectable level of WalliKnowledge. You've won a biscuit!*

11 POINTS

But that's impossible because there are only ten questions. You're getting a GRADE F, you cheat!

This whiteboard is faulty

ANSWERS ON PAGE 76

* Biscuit not included

JANET CRUMB

Hello, dirty unwashed member of the public,

I'm Janet Crumb. Have we met? I am delighted to make your acquaintance and I would very much like you to vote for me to be your MP. As you might not be very educated, I should point out that "MP" stands for Member of Parliament. It most certainly does not stand for Massive Poohead, which is what some local oiks have nicknamed me.

You are most likely not as clever as me (i.e. you're stupider) so why not leave all the important decisions to me? I'll make Britain great again for you. Here are my policies for a Better Britain.

A TOTAL BAN ON JUNK FOOD

No burgers, no hot dogs, no cold dogs, no fried chicken, no stuffed-crust pizza, no unstuffed-crust pizza, and definitely no chips. Anyone caught eating any of these foods will be imprisoned and given a diet of raw broccoli and sprouts.

NO MORE BALL GAMES

And, while I'm at it, no balls. And no games, either.

NEW CINEMA REGULATIONS

The only film allowed to be shown will be *The Sound of Music* – and any scary bits (e.g. when a dog bites, or a bee stings) will be heavily censored so as not to corrupt the minds of our young people.

AN END TO PICTURE BOOKS

For decades, books have been made to look silly, with lots of stupid pictures distracting you from the words. I pledge to make all books full of words only. Ideally long and complicated ones, like "pontifical".

ONE-TOY LIMIT

Children will be made to choose their favourite toy (no bigger than a shoebox). All of their remaining toys will then be melted down to make traffic cones. This will result in: a) fewer spoiled children, and b) more traffic cones.

REMOVE ALL CUTE CAT VIDEOS FROM YOUTUBE

They're a waste of everyone's time. All that time the lower classes spend watching cat videos could be used for something more constructive, such as descaling your kettle or creosoting a fence.

NO NEW MUSIC

We've got enough music now – we don't need any more. You can have just as much fun at a disco dancing to Beethoven as you can body bopping to pop music.

IMPROVED EDUCATION

School pupils currently don't work hard enough, so I will be extending the school hours so class begins at 6 a.m. and finishes at 9 p.m., with a three-minute lunch break. These hours will of course be relaxed on Sundays, when the lunch break will be extended to four minutes to let children unwind.

FREE BROCCOLI

Every child will receive a free piece of raw broccoli through the post every day and it will become a legal requirement for them to eat each and every one.

AN END TO DOG "DOINGS"

There will be no more dog "doings" on our pavements as I shall be banning dogs.

SAFE PLAY AREAS

The town's playgrounds will be made safe for our precious kiddywinks by the removal of any elements that could be dangerous. These include swings, slides, roundabouts, seesaws, climbing frames, springy motorbikes/horses, sandpits, splash parks and grass (some children are allergic to it).

so VOTE FOR JANET CRUMB!

TOGETHER WE CAN MAKE BRITAIN BOTH MORE JANETY AND MORE CRUMBY.

LEONARD SPUD'S
GUIDE TO
LOO-ROLL MODELLING

Joe Spud's prized possession is a loo-roll rocket made by his dad, Leonard Spud.

A LOO-ROLL ROLLING PIN*
LOO ROLLS REQUIRED: 3

INSTRUCTIONS: Just stick three loo rolls together in a row. That's it. This is the perfect loo-roll model to make if you're a beginner.
* Do not try to roll food with this as it will make the food smell of toilets.

A LOO-ROLL RACING CAR
LOO ROLLS REQUIRED: 8

INSTRUCTIONS: Use loo rolls for the wheels, but for the chassis… also use loo rolls. Loo-roll engine optional.
To capture the feel of a real Formula One race, every half an hour hurriedly yank off the loo-roll wheels from your loo-roll racing car, then speedily replace them with four fresh new loo rolls, ideally in under 3.7 seconds.

A LOO-ROLL FORT AND LOO-ROLL SOLDIERS
LOO ROLLS REQUIRED: 48 IN TOTAL – 36 (FORT)
12 (SOLDIERS)

INSTRUCTIONS: Use loo rolls to build the outer walls, then, for the turrets, use loo rolls. However, this is where things take a turn, so pay close attention. For the soldiers, use loo rolls that you've painted. To make your loo-roll fort like a real fort, pour water round it to create a moat.
(Please note: unlike a real fort, this will make your loo-roll fort go soggy.)

A LOO-ROLL TELESCOPE
LOO ROLLS REQUIRED: 4

INSTRUCTIONS: To the untrained eye, this might look very similar to the loo-roll rolling pin. But, to an expert loo-roll modeller, it's markedly different because instead of using THREE loo rolls, this model uses FOUR, which is 33.3% more loo rolls. Never ever try to use your loo-roll telescope as a loo-roll rolling pin as this may have disastrous, possibly even fatal, consequences.

A LOO-ROLL SPACE ROCKET
LOO ROLLS REQUIRED: 7

INSTRUCTIONS: Use four loo rolls for the rocket base. But to make the shaft of the rocket I am using a very specialist building material – loo rolls. It is actually possible to launch this loo-roll rocket into space. All you need to do is attach it to a real NASA rocket with Blu-tack. If you don't live near the Kennedy Space Center in Florida (or you do, but don't have any spare Blu-tack), just ask a parent with a very strong arm to throw it as high as they can.

A LOO-ROLL LOO
LOO ROLLS REQUIRED: 426

INSTRUCTIONS: I think the picture is pretty self-explanatory. Just stick the loo rolls together until they look like that. WARNING: Do not try to use this loo-roll loo as a loo. It is not plumbed in, so anything that is splashed or plopped into it will totally ruin the cardboard. I found that out the hard way.

JOE SPUD'S LETTER TO SANTA

DEAR SANTA,

My name is Joe Spud and I am eleven years old. Even though I hate my school, St Cuthbert's School for Boys (note: please put all of my teachers on the naughty list) and I haven't got any real friends, I have still been good this year.

For my last birthday my dad, who's a billionaire, gave me a £1,000,000 cheque. But you're magical so I expect you'll get me something even more expensive. It can be quite tricky buying a present for me, because I have so much stuff already. So I thought I'd be kind and helpful by giving you some suggestions for things I haven't got yet.

JOE SPUD'S CHRISTMAS LIST

1. A GLASS TANK BIG ENOUGH TO FIT A BLUE WHALE
2. A PET BLUE WHALE (IDEALLY HOUSE-TRAINED)
3. A RADIO-CONTROLLED HELICOPTER (LIFE-SIZE)
4. SHUT DOWN THE M25 — SO I CAN USE IT AS A GO-KART TRACK WHENEVER I WANT
5. MY OWN PERSONALISED STAR WARS MOVIE: EPISODE 6½, WHICH SHOWS WHAT HAPPENED BETWEEN RETURN OF THE JEDI AND THE FORCE AWAKENS (NO ONE MUST BE ALLOWED TO WATCH THIS MOVIE APART FROM ME, NOT EVEN THE DIRECTOR, WHO MUST MAKE IT WITH THEIR EYES CLOSED)
6. A MALDIVE ISLAND (ONE OF THE BIGGER ONES)
7. A PAIR OF VOICE-CONTROLLED-WI-FI-HOVER-AIR-CUSHIONED TRAINERS — THEY'RE NOT INVENTED YET AND I'M NOT ENTIRELY SURE WHAT THEY DO, BUT I KNOW YOUR ELVES WILL FIGURE IT OUT
8. A SNOWBOARD (AND A GIANT SNOW MACHINE AND A BEN NEVIS)
9. A £15,000,000 BOOK TOKEN
10. ALL OF YOUR REINDEER
11. A FRIEND — ONE WHO LIKES ME FOR ME, NOT FOR MY MONEY

I don't expect you to get me EVERYTHING on the list. So if you can only get me one thing, I'd like it to be number 11. However, if you can't get me that, I'll make do with all the other ten things.

Merry Christmas.

Yours expectantly,

JOE SPUD

P.S. ON CHRISTMAS EVE, CHECK BY THE FIREPLACE BECAUSE I WILL LEAVE YOU A GLASS OF MILK, A MINCE PIE AND A ROLL OF LIMITED-EDITION CHRISTMAS BUMFRESH LOO PAPER (IT SMELLS OF CINNAMON, TURKEY AND BRUSSELS SPROUTS).

THE MOST SPECTACULAR WEDDING OF THE CENTURY!*

DEMON DENTIST

* The most spectacular wedding of the century between a person called Winnie and a person called Raj.

The biggest event in the newsagent-wedding calendar occurred last weekend when bride, Winnie, (full name Winnie Prophecy Mystelle Passionfruit Turquoise Dave Smith) married her groom Raj (full name Raj).

CANARY

The bride wore a dazzling canary-yellow dress with way too many bustles and layers, and a long frilly train. The groom, who had been dressed by the bride, wore a top hat and tails and was not very happy about it. The pageboy, their adopted son, Alfie, was dressed in a fancy sailor suit. He looked even less happy about it.

DISCOUNTED

The ceremony itself was beautiful. The couple had written their own vows, which included the question "Do you sell heavily discounted sweets and crisps?" to which Raj responded, "I do." The vows also included the question "Do you promise to wear outrageously colourful clothing in sickness and in health?" to which Winnie responded, "I do." Then the bride kissed the groom. Then the groom kissed the minister, because he hadn't fully understood the ceremony, but fortunately the minister didn't seem to mind.

UNUSUAL HYMN

Due to an organisational mix-up involving the song intended for the couple's first dance, and very much to the surprise of the congregation, the hymn for the ceremony was "Gangnam Style". The churchgoers' attempts to pronounce the mainly Korean lyrics were admirable, and some even did the appropriate dance moves. Including the minister.

REVELS

The wedding breakfast buffet was a delightful spread specially prepared by the groom. Starters were vintage Twiglets from 2008 (a very good year for Twiglets). The main was a choice of smoky-bacon crisps (for meat-eaters) or cheese-and-onion crisps (for vegetarians). And dessert was a wide selection of out-of-date Revels (no more than one per guest). The attendees were also treated to a Tizer fountain, which is where you make a pyramid of champagne glasses, then tip a three-litre bottle of Tizer into the top glass. When the Tizer ran out, the groom moved on to Lilt, which created a murky brown fizzy tropical cocktail. Any of the weird drink that spilled on to the tablecloth was mopped up and squeezed back into the bottle and sold as "Discount Home-made Mocktail".

STALE

The wedding cake was a twelve-tier creation made exclusively from Jaffa Cakes. It tasted delicious, though the cakey bits had gone a bit stale, so it was actually more like a twelve-tier wedding biscuit. Both bride and groom struggled to cut into the cake, so instead the Jaffa Cakes were used as coasters on which guests could place their glasses of muddy Lilt-Tizer.

FIRST DANCE

Due to the aforementioned musical mix-up, the couple's first dance was to the hymn "All Things Bright and Beautiful". This made for a peculiar sight – Winnie and Raj quickly discovered it's quite tricky doing "Gangnam Style" dance moves to a hymn.

MOPED

The happy couple set off from the reception (with Alfie) to embark on their honeymoon, a luxury seven-day moped cruise, taking in Britain's most spectacular and historic newsagent's and charity shops.

BEHIND THE SCENES!

TOP SECRET
INFO
Eat pages after reading.

EXTRA EXCLUSIVELY EXCLUSIVES

David Walliams

WALLIAMS SWIMS!
DAVID'S DIARY

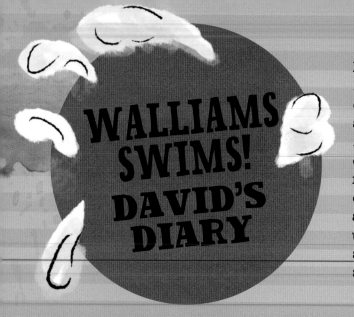

Dear reader,
It's me, David Walliams: writer, comedian, TV judge and spy (but I'm not allowed to tell anyone I'm a spy, because it's a secret). I'm also known for my charity swims. I don't like to talk about my charity swims too much because my charity swims aren't about me. They're about charity. And swimming. Swimming which I did. For charity. Here are the swims I did for charity and how far I swam:

- THE STRAIT OF GIBRALTAR - 12 MILES
- THE ENGLISH CHANNEL - 22 MILES
- THE THAMES - 140 MILES ←
- WIMBLEDON LEISURE CENTRE - 10 METRES (BACKSTROKE)

As a special treat, I thought I'd share with you an extract from the training diary I kept for my Thames swim, in case you, like me, ever go mad and want to swim 140 miles.

15 NOVEMBER 2010
Today is the first day of training. I sat with my bum in the sink for ten minutes. You've got to start somewhere. (But I didn't like it. My bum's wet now, and I don't really like water.)

15 FEBRUARY 2011
I've been training for three months and have now progressed to sitting in the bath. Tomorrow I will try putting water in it.

16 FEBRUARY 2011
After a lot of crying, I finally managed to sit in a bath with water in it. I eventually plucked up the courage to swim one length of the bath... which I did by leaning forward and touching the taps. Success!

28 JUNE 2011
I have had a great few months. I progressed from swimming in the bath to standing in a pond. Although there were frogs in the pond and when I saw them I cried and ran back into the house.

19 JULY 2011
Today I suffered a bit of a setback. I tried to bribe my lookalike to do the swim for me instead. He said yes, which is amazing, because my lookalike is Olympic diver Tom Daley. (The similarities between the two of us are uncanny.) Unfortunately, the charity swim is between 5 and 12 September and Tom has tickets to go to a pop concert on 9 September, so he can't make it. Looks like I'm going to have to do the swim myself after all.

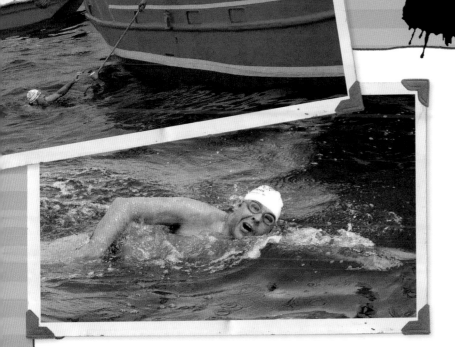

26 AUGUST 2011

Yet another setback. I asked the head of Sport Relief if, rather than swim the Thames, I could go down it in a boat. More specifically a yacht with a cinema room. He said that was cheating. I disagreed. We wrestled. He won. I still have to do the swim.

2 SEPTEMBER 2011

Today I put on my swimming trunks and covered myself in goose fat. Then I thought, "You know what? While I'm dressed like this, I should probably go for a swim." (Note: people think that I smear goose fat on me to keep myself warm while swimming. That's not the case. It's actually because I love dogs – and to attract them I like to run around Regent's Park covered in goose fat. Then, when dogs run up and lick me, I steal them. I now have 200 dogs. Hopefully I'll catch some more dogs on my swim.) Anyway, where was I? Oh yes. The swim was OK, but I went the wrong way along the Thames and ended up in France, which could be a problem because I don't have my passport.

5 SEPTEMBER 2011

Today is the big day. It is important to eat well before you do a lot of exercise as your body uses up a lot of energy. So yesterday I ate desserts all day. I do this anyway. But yesterday was different because an actual doctor told me to do it. At least I think he was a doctor. He was wearing a chef's hat and worked in Barry's Bakery, but as he filled my bag with buns and cakes he pinky-promised me he was a doctor. That's good enough for me! So I've got chocolate cake round my mouth, I'm in my trunks and I'm covered in goose fat. Time for me to end my training and do the swim for real. Wish me luck! Actually, I've just felt the water – it's cold... I might just not do it.

I did do it. But only because there were TV cameras and I didn't want to look like a wally. I hope these extracts help any future swimmers to live their dream and swim any stretch of water they want to. Right, I'm off to Regent's Park to catch myself another dog. Bye!

David Walliams

THE WORLD OF DAVID WALLIAMS ON SCREEN:
BEHIND THE SCENES

Dear reader,
As well as reading my books, you may have seen some of my stories
on television, or even on DVD in the bargain bin at a petrol
station. And now, exclusively to this book, I can reveal some of the
director's fun facts from behind the scenes of those TV programmes.
For example, did you know that, despite what it looks like, people
on TV are actually normal-sized and not flat? And did you know that
sometimes people on TV use made-up names and pretend to be someone
they're not? While you and I would call that "lying", on television
they call it "acting". Here are some more fascinating facts from
behind the scenes on the TV adaptations.

David Walliams

Billionaire Boy

DAVID WALLIAMS AS "MRS TRAFE" IN *BILLIONAIRE BOY*

FUN FACT: The costume department had
a special dinner-lady outfit hired for
David, but he arrived dressed like this
so they didn't need to use it.

FUN FACT: The whisk in the picture is
normal-sized. David is actually only
three feet, two inches tall.

DAVID WALLIAMS AS "MRS TRAFE" IN *BILLIONAIRE BOY*

FUN FACT: The out-of-focus lady in the back
right of this photo is in fact Her Majesty the
Queen, who had a non-speaking cameo in one scene.
Unfortunately, that scene was subsequently cut
from the finished programme.

FUN FACT: After *Billionaire Boy* was screened on
BBC1, Mrs Trafe's cupcake-themed tabard became
the most-desired fashion item in the world. Twelve
Hollywood celebrities were seen wearing it at that
year's Oscars.

DAVID WALLIAMS AS "MRS TRAFE" IN *BILLIONAIRE BOY*

FUN FACT: The director asked David Walliams to pull his happiest face and this was his best attempt.

FUN FACT: David Walliams doesn't own a washing machine. So, in this picture, he's not cooking a meal – he's boiling his underpants.

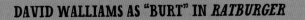

Ratburger

DAVID WALLIAMS AS "BURT" IN *RATBURGER*

FUN FACT: The van in this picture is actually owned by David and he unsurprisingly makes more money selling burgers than he does from his books.

FUN FACT: To fully get into the role of "Burt", David ate up to eight ratburgers a day. After the show was finished, David returned to his normal diet – which is fifteen ratburgers a day.

DAVID WALLIAMS AND SHERIDAN SMITH AS "BURT" AND "SHEILA" IN *RATBURGER*

FUN FACT: Sheridan's "hair" was in fact candyfloss, which David and the rest of the cast liked to nibble on between takes.

FUN FACT: Sheridan Smith is actually one metre taller than David Walliams, so in all their scenes together David was standing on a milk crate while Sheridan stood in a specially dug trench.

Ratburger

DAVID WALLIAMS AS "BURT" IN *RATBURGER*

FUN FACT: If you have a rat in a box, you can hold it out at arm's length and strengthen your triceps. Repeat twice a day with both arms if you want to look like David Walliams.

FUN FACT: On one day of filming, David's lunchbox got confused with this rat trap. Bad news: David got halfway into his "lunch" before he realised. Good news: the rat trainer got a free sandwich, a cheese triangle and a lollipop.

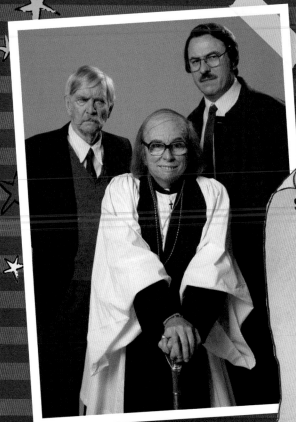

Grandpa's Great Escape

SIR TOM COURTENAY, JENNIFER SAUNDERS AND DAVID WALLIAMS AS "GRANDPA", "REVEREND FINE" AND "BARRY" IN *GRANDPA'S GREAT ESCAPE*

FUN FACT: The twice Oscar-nominated actor Sir Tom Courtenay won a competition on the back of a cereal box to play "Grandpa" in *Grandpa's Great Escape*.

FUN FACT: Jennifer Saunders actually became an ordained reverend to play this role. After filming, she held a ceremony in which she married Sir Tom Courtenay and his now-husband David Walliams-Courtenay.

DAVID WALLIAMS, JENNIFER SAUNDERS AND SIR TOM COURTENAY AS "BARRY", "MISS DANDY" AND "GRANDPA" IN *GRANDPA'S GREAT ESCAPE*

FUN FACT: David Walliams is standing on a box here because he always insists on being the tallest person in every photo. That's why you'll never see him photographed beside basketball players, Dwayne "The Rock" Johnson or a giraffe.

FUN FACT: Oscar-nominated actor Sir Tom Courtenay got up late for filming on this day – that's why he's still wearing his dressing gown.

DAVID WALLIAMS AS "BARRY" IN *GRANDPA'S GREAT ESCAPE*

FUN FACT: This orange phone is a direct line to Batman. He never answers, but I promise it does go through to his Batcave.

FUN FACT: David refuses to ever shave off his moustache. So if you ever see him without one it means that millions of pounds have been spent on computer graphics to make him look clean-shaven.

SIR TOM COURTENAY AND KIT CONNOR AS "GRANDPA" AND "JACK" IN *GRANDPA'S GREAT ESCAPE*

FUN FACT: As a prank, David Walliams put superglue on both actors' fingernails, which is why their hands are stuck to their heads like this.

FUN FACT: The aircraft used during filming is what military aviation historians call, in technical jargon, "a green plane".

GREYBRIDGE SCHOOL REPORT

NAME: **David Walliams**

SUBJECT	REMARKS	GRADE
ENGLISH *Mr Wordsworth*	David loves writing stories – so it's a real shame he's so bad at it. All his tales just have two-word titles like, "Magic Mum", "Untidy Uncle" and "Terrible Teacher". By the way, his last story about an ineffective English teacher called Mr Wordsworth was highly unbelievable. Us English teachers are actually very competent and never make mistaks.	F
DRAMA *Miss Tree*	David is very shy and retiring. No matter how hard I try, I can't seem to get him out of his shell. There was one time that he did make everyone laugh – when he told us he wanted to work in showbusiness. Hilarious! However, David relishes passing comment on whether other pupils are good or bad, so maybe one day he'll have a career as a judge? (I mean in a courtroom, obviously, because reality TV talent-show judges haven't been invented yet.)	F
HISTORY *Miss Castle*	David is useless at remembering key events and dates, though he does love turning up to lessons in historical attire. Yesterday he arrived dressed as Queen Elizabeth I, but his giant dress became wedged in the classroom door, preventing any other pupils getting in. The lesson consequently had to be cancelled.	F
PE *Mr Foxon*	David takes his swimming so seriously that he even covers himself in goose fat before lessons. This hasn't gone down well with the staff at the leisure centre, who have informed the school that we can no longer use their facilities.	F

Subject	Remarks	Grade
GEOGRAPHY *Miss Mapp*	David's geographical knowledge is so bad that he has yet to find my classroom.	F
MATHS *Ms Adding*	David was terrible at maths, but he has recently shown some improvement. When I offered him ten doughnuts and took away three, he immediately knew how many were missing. Then he ate all ten doughnuts. And my packed lunch. And my secret supply of biscuits. I've never been so hungry.	F
COOKERY *Mr Spoon*	David is a creative chef who uses an array of different and experimental ingredients. Unfortunately, his latest concoction gave several of his classmates food poisoning, which is why I have now banned pupils from making ratburgers ever again.	F
SCIENCE *Mr Tin*	I can only speak extremely highly of David. But that's because he filled my lab with helium gas. His fellow pupils find my squeaky voice hilarious and now won't take anything I say seriously.	F

Head teacher's comments

Miss Grave

I have never seen so many Fs on a single report card. Nevertheless, as a head teacher I feel it's my duty to look for the positives, so let me just say this: David has performed very consistently across his subjects. To be brutally honest, it's apparent that David can neither act nor write – so one thing's for sure: he won't be making it on screen or as a writer any time soon.

Miss Grave

ANSWERS

PAGES 10–11

David Walliams'
Inside His Writing Shed

THERE ARE **14** DIFFERENCES BETWEEN THE TWO PICTURES. SPOT THEM ALL.

The world of David Walliams MAP

PAGES 12–13

1) *Ratburger* and *Bad Dad*
2) The National Trouser Museum – although it does sound EXCELLENT
3) A billion pounds – Joe Spud from *Billionaire Boy*
4) Gilbert Goodie from *Bad Dad*
5) Ben's from *Gangsta Granny*
6) The Midnight Gang
7) Mr Stink
8) Zoe from *Ratburger*
9) St Agatha's School for Aristocratic Girls
10) Find him yourself...*

PAGE 48

AUNTIE ALBERTA'S OWLEUM MEMORY CHALLENGE

PLAYER ONE
1) False. It is 1mm tall.
2) King Henry VIII
3) Eight seconds

PLAYER TWO
1) 1mm
2) *Tyrannorowlus rex*
3) 101 owl screeches

PAGE 43

THE BURT & SHEILA *RATBURGER* QUIZ!

BURT

SHEILA

1) C
2) B
3) C
4) C
5) B
6) C
7) C
8) A
9) C
10) C

PAGES 56–57

KEY STAGE 27 in the world of David Walliams Studies Advanced Level: Unit 1

Q1
ANSWER: B – One. Gingernut in *Ratburger* dies and gets chucked in the bin by Sheila.

Q2
ANSWER: B – Mini. I think. I can't remember. Would you mind checking for me? Thanks.

Q3
ANSWER: C. At least Burt's disease-ridden burgers and Mrs Trafe's noxious school dinners are confined to the UK. David Walliams travels all around the world visiting schools, pretending to talk about his books, but his real motive is to do as many blow-offs in assemblies as possible.

Q4
ANSWER: B. And also C.

Q5
ANSWER: C. It starts on page 157 and finally finishes 1,343 letters later at the bottom of page 160. Here's how long it is:

HahahahahahahahahahahahahaHahahahahahahahahahah
hahahahahaHahahahahahahahahahahahahahahahahHahahah
ahahahahahahahahahahahahahahahahaHhahahahahahahaha
hahahahahaahahahahHahahahahahahahahahahahahahahahah
ahHahahahahahahahahahaahahahahahahahahahH Hahahahaha
hahahahahahahahahhahahahahahahaHahahahahahahahahaha
hahahahahahaHahahahahahahhahahahahahahahahahahahah
Hahahahahahahahahahahahahahahahahahahahhhahahahaha
hahahahahahahahahahHahahahahahahahahahahahahahahHaha
hahahahahahahahahahahahahahahahahaHahahahahahahahah
ahahahahahahahahHahahahahahahahahahahahahahhhahahah
HahahahahahahahahahhahahahahahahahahahahahahahahHahahahaha
hahaahahahahahhahahahahahahahahahhahahahahahahahahaha
hahahaHahahahahahahahahahahahahahahahahahahahahahah
ahaHahahahaahahahahahahahahahahahahahahahahahahahah
ahahahahahahahahahahahahahahaHahahahahahahahahahahah
ahahHahahahahahahahahahahahahahahahahahahahahahahah
ahHahahahahahahahahahahahahahahahahahahahahaahahah
ahahahahahahahahahahahahahahahahahahahahahaHahahahah
ahahahahahahahahahahahahahahahaHahahahahahahahahaHa
hahahahahahahahahahahahahahahahahahahahahahahahah
Hahahahahahahahahahahahahahahahahahahahahahahahhhah
ahahahahahahahahahahaahahaHahahahahahahahahahahahahah
HahahahahahahahahahahahahahahahahahahahaHhahahahaha
hahahahahahahahahahahHahahahahahahahahahahahahahahhhah
ahahHahahahahahahahahahahahahahahahahahahahahahHahah
ahahahahahhhahahahahahahahaHahhahahahahahahahahahahaH
ahahahahahaha!

Q6
ANSWER: B. However, for getting this question correct, you DO win a Crown Jewel of your choosing. Just go to the Tower of London and help yourself. The Beefeaters won't mind at all, honest.

Q7
ANSWER: B. Although it's only a matter of time before Raj decides to branch out from the newsagent business and go into beauty treatments.

Q8
ANSWER: A. But if you want to know a highly top-secret secret, David also originally wrote *Harry Potter and the Philosopher's Stone*, but he didn't think it was any good so he threw it into a bin in a park, which is where J. K. Rowling found it.

Q9
ANSWER: B. However, by including Nurse Nincompoop in this test, she has now technically featured in a David Walliams book, but let's not give that any more thought.

Q10
ANSWER: B. Although if David's brain is preserved in vinegar and connected to the internet, he could well keep producing new books for thousands of years to come.

* Just joking. He is behind the tree opposite the Crumbs' residence.

WHAT TO DO WITH

Here are some ideas for what you could do with this book now you've finished reading it.

Attach it to a helium balloon and send it into space so that other civilisations may learn how intelligent human beings are.

Shred the book and use it as bedding for a pet hamster or gerbil.

If you've forgotten to buy your mum a birthday present, tear out a page and fashion her some earrings.

Stand on it to reach something VERY slightly out of reach.

Open up a fish and chip shop, then use these pages to wrap up the fish and chips you sell.

Start a multi-billion-pound online shopping company, then shred the pages and use them as needlessly bulky packaging for a small item, such as a mint.

Try to turn it back into a tree.

Convert it into a yoga mat for a squirrel.

Why not cut out all the letters and rearrange them to make another book, e.g. *Dracula* by Bram Stoker?

If you run out of toilet paper, simply pull out the pages and wipe your bottom with them.